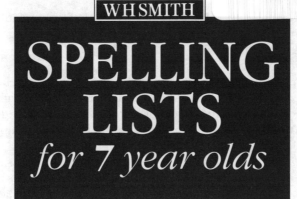

WH SMITH

SPELLING LISTS
for 7 year olds

Louis Fidge

Published exclusively for W H Smith by Ginn

Notes for parents

The Spelling List series of books is designed to help your children improve their spelling, and to fit in with the requirements for Spelling in the National Curriculum for English.

The books provide a framework of spelling activities for developing and practising basic spelling skills in an enjoyable and educationally effective way. The words taught are the sort of words most frequently used by children in their writing and take into account the word groups stipulated in the Curriculum guidelines for English.

Ten Target words, containing the spelling pattern or patterns to be introduced, are highlighted at the top of the page. The activities which follow practise and reinforce the spelling in a variety of ways. Frequently Challenges are set to encourage children to think further or to use a dictionary. Test Yourself pages are included to check on spellings taught. As each page is completed get your child to fill in the Record Sheet on page 32 to keep a check on progress made, stimulate further effort and provide a sense of achievement.

Encourage your child to use the spelling strategy outlined below when tackling new words. Always offer positive praise and encouragement as your child is working through the book.

Notes for children

Follow these five simple rules to help you with your spelling.

1   **LOOK** carefully at the word you want to learn. Pick out any word patterns you know. Are there any smaller words within the word?

2   **SAY** the word. Does it sound the way it looks?

3   **COVER** the word with your hand. Try to see the word in your head.

4   **WRITE** the word from memory. Do not copy the word letter by letter.

5   **CHECK** to see if you spelt it correctly.

2

Target words

~~chips~~	~~ship~~	rip	sip	~~trip~~
~~big~~	~~dig~~	fig	~~pig~~	~~wig~~

1 Use some of the words to finish the sentences.

We saw a ___Ship___ sailing on the sea.

A _____ is a kind of fruit.

My dog likes to ___dig___ in the garden.

I fell and hurt my ___big___ toe.

The man wore a ___Wig___ on his head.

The ___pig___ lived in a sty on the farm.

We went on a ___trip___ to the seaside.

Do you want fish and ___Chips___ for tea?

2 Finish these words with **ip** or **ig**.

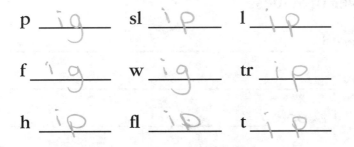

p ___ig___   sl ___ip___   l ___ip___

f ___ig___   w ___ig___   tr ___ip___

h ___ip___   fl ___ip___   t ___ip___

Challenge   Can you write a sentence using some **ig** words?

5

rob	pot	rot
cot	sob	bob
got	mob	hot
	job	

1 Colour the **ob** words yellow. Colour the **ot** words red.

2 Find some **ob** and **ot** words in these long words.

robot   spotted   forgot

brother   Scotland   sobbing

3 Answer the clues.

Not cold _____ hot _____

To cry _____ cry _____

A lot of people _____

Something you cook in _____

Where a baby sleeps _____

The work you do _____

6

Target words

gun	bun	fun	sun	run
jug	dug	tug	mug	slug

1 Write the **un** words in the circle.
Write the **ug** words in the square.

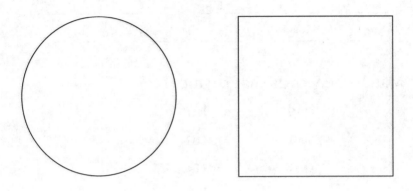

2 Finish these words with **un** or **ug**.

d_____   s_____   sl_____

f_____   t_____   j_____

3 Instead of the **b** in **but**, write c, h, n, p and sh.

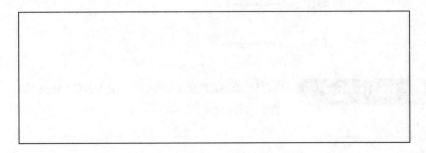

7

bag	tin	top	but	hut
rag	red	hop	pin	bed

1 Write out the words from the box.

    __a__   __e__   __i__   __o__   __u__

    __a__   __e__   __i__   __o__   __u__

2 Match the words that rhyme.

        bag   but

        red   tin

        pin   rag

        top   bed

        hut   hop

3 Write a different rhyming word.

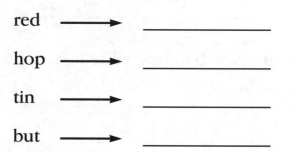

        red ⟶ _____

        hop ⟶ _____

        tin ⟶ _____

        but ⟶ _____

Challenge Write a sentence using two words that rhyme.

TEST YOURSELF

what	than	when	get	trip
dig	hot	sob	fun	jug

1 Find the words in the word square.

a	b	h	o	t	c	d	f	u	n
e	f	g	h	w	h	e	n	i	j
w	h	a	t	k	l	m	p	r	s
t	v	g	e	t	w	s	o	b	x
y	z	a	b	t	r	i	p	c	d
e	d	i	g	f	g	h	j	e	t
n	o	p	t	h	a	n	a	n	p
e	v	e	r	y	j	u	g	i	s

My score ☐ out of 10

2 • Look carefully at the words in the box.
   • Cover the top of the page.
   • Write as many of the words without copying as you can.
   • Check your spellings.

My score ☐ out of 10

9

Target words

by	my	dry	fly	why
daisy	baby	lily	tiny	jelly

1 Add **y** to make the words on the steps.

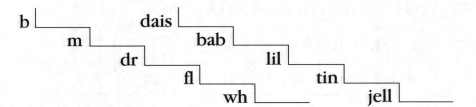

2 Answer the clues.

An insect_____

A question word _____

The opposite of wet _____

Something you can eat _____

Very small_____

Two kinds of flowers _____

A young child_____

3 Which two words are left over?

me	he	they	them	us
we	she	her	him	you

1 Write the words that rhyme with **me**.

_____

2 Write the words that contain **he**.

_____

3 Write any words with a **u** in them.

_____

4 Write any words with **the** in them.

_____

5 Which word is left over?

_____

Challenge  Make a list of some more words that rhyme with **me**.

_____

_____

11

| here | there | when | then | what |
| who | why | where | which | how |

1 Write the words beginning with **wh**.

_____

_____

2 Write the words containing **here**.

_____

3 Write the words containing **he**.

_____

_____

4 Write any words with **hen** or **hat** in them.

_____

5 Which word is left over?

_____

Challenge Find all the question words in the box. Write a sentence for each one.

Target words

ball	tell	yell	shall	fall
wall	shell	fell	well	call

1 Write the words on the wall.

all words

b_____	sh_____	f_____	w_____	c_____

ell words

t_____	y_____	f_____	sh_____	w_____

2 Write the words in alphabetical order.

all words   **ell** words

1 _____   1 _____

2 _____   2 _____

3 _____   3 _____

4 _____   4 _____

5 _____   5 _____

3 Find some short **all** and **ell** words in the long words below.

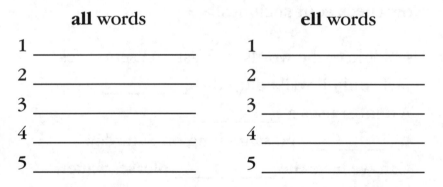

yellow	falling	balloon
fellow	shallow	wellington

13

fill	bill	hill	pill	drill
still	grill	kill	will	mill

1 Cover the words above and write them without copying.

1	_____	6	_____
2	_____	7	_____
3	_____	8	_____
4	_____	9	_____
5	_____	10	_____

Now check your spellings!

2 Use some of the words to finish the sentences.

Jack and Jill walked up the _____.

A dentist uses a _____.

I _____ go swimming on Saturday.

Can we have the _____ please, waiter?

Challenge Write a sentence using as many **ill** words as you can.

luck   black   sack   stuck   truck

pack   quack   duck   pluck   back

1 Do these word sums.

b + ack = _____   d + uck = _____

bl + ack = _____   l + uck = _____

p + ack = _____   pl + uck = _____

qu + ack = _____   tr + uck = _____

s + ack = _____   st + uck = _____

2 Use some of the words to finish the crossword.

Across
3 The noise a duck makes
5 A colour
6 Part of the body

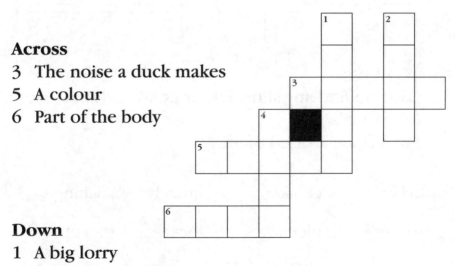

Down
1 A big lorry
2 A _____ of wolves
4 A large bag

rock	kick	shock	clock	brick
sock	tick	lock	chick	quick

1 Write the **ick** and **ock** words on the correct ladders.

ick   **ock**

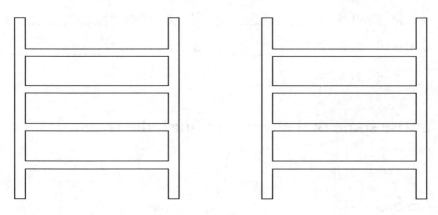

2 Can you find any short **ick** or **ock** words in these long words?
Put a circle around them.

ticket   chicken   quickly   sticking

socket   blockage   locker   rocket

                clicked   thicket

TEST YOURSELF

they	where	still	black	what
stuck	which	quick	ball	clock

1 Write the words which:

begin with st

Still , stuck ,

end with ck

black stuck clock quick

end with ll

Still Ball

begin with wh

where what which

Which word is left over?

they

My score ☐ out of 10

2 • Close your book.
• Write as many of the words
without copying as you can.
• Check your spellings.

My score ☐ out of 10

17

bang	sung	fling	clang	rung
wing	bring	long	strong	king

1   **Choose**   **Complete**   **Write**

Choose	Complete	Write
i or u	w__ng	wing
o or a	cl__ng	_____
e or u	s__ng	_____
o or i	l__ng	_____
a or o	str__ng	_____
u or e	r__ng	_____
e or a	b__ng	_____
i or u	k__ng	_____
o or i	fl__ng	_____
i or o	br__ng	_____

2 Join the rhyming words.

clang	wing
sung	strong
long	bang
fling	rung

Challenge   Write some more words ending in **ng**. Add the words that rhyme to the list above.

18

Target words

old	milk	mild	wild	yolk
silk	hold	walk	chalk	bold

1 Sort these words into the correct columns.

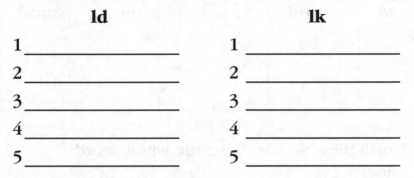

ld	lk
1_____	1_____
2_____	2_____
3_____	3_____
4_____	4_____
5_____	5_____

2 Use some of the words to finish the crossword.

Across
3 Something you get from cows
4 We took the dog for a _____ in the park yesterday.

Down
1 The yellow part of an egg
2 A soft shiny material

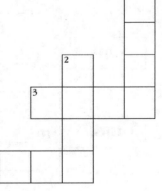

Challenge How many words can you think of that have **old** in them, like **gold**en?

19

Target words

fond	hand	bend	fund	sand
kind	find	band	bond	mend

1 Write the words in the correct boxes.

and	**end**	**ind**	**ond**	**und**

2 Finish these words. Write the whole word underneath.

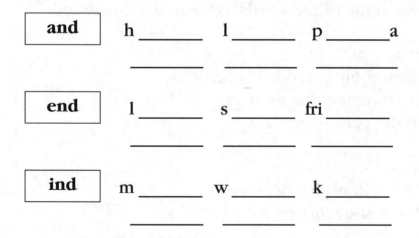

and	h _____	l _____	p _____ a
	_____	_____	_____

end	l _____	s _____	fri _____
	_____	_____	_____

ind	m _____	w _____	k _____
	_____	_____	_____

Challenge Write some sentences using as many **and**, **end**, **ind**, **ond** and **und** words as you can.

think	bank	junk	sank	blink
thank	drunk	pink	blank	honk

1   **Choose**   **Complete**   **Write**

Choose	Complete	Write
a or i	b__nk	_____
e or o	h__nk	_____
o or u	j__nk	_____
e or a	s__nk	_____
u or i	bl__nk	_____
i or e	th__nk	_____
u or a	th__nk	_____
e or u	dr__nk	_____
o or a	bl__nk	_____
a or i	p__nk	_____

2 Join the rhyming words.

bank	sack
trunk	blank
silk	pink
black	milk
think	sunk

Challenge   Add other rhyming words ending in **k** to the list above.

Target words

lamp	help	dark	belt	curl
damp	park	melt	girl	felt

1 Choose one of these letters to finish each word.

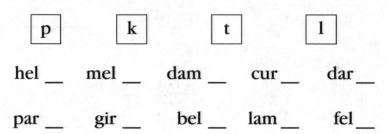

p	k	t	l

hel __   mel __   dam __   cur __   dar __

par __   gir __   bel __   lam __   fel __

2 Write as many of the words without copying as you can.

3 Use some of the words to answer the clues.

Without light_____

Slightly wet _____

Something you wear around the waist_____

A green open space in a city _____

A twisted lock of hair_____

22

was	very	thing	any	some
one	many	want	every	home

1 Write the words which:

contain **ery**

_____

begin with **wa**

_____

end with **ny**

_____

end with **ome**

_____

2 Do these word sums.

any + one = anyone

some + one =

every + one =

any + thing =

some + thing =

every + thing =

Challenge Can you think up any more words
beginning with **any**, **some**,
or **every**?

TEST YOURSELF

some	sand	cling	think	golden
film	wild	every	milk	strong

1 Find the words in the word square.

y	s	a	n	d	b	c	d	e	f
b	t	i	n	k	t	h	i	n	k
c	r	n	a	p	m	k	j	h	g
s	o	m	e	v	e	r	t	s	h
e	n	a	c	a	v	a	u	e	o
n	g	o	l	d	e	n	d	m	e
d	r	u	i	f	r	x	y	d	e
e	g	h	n	m	y	f	i	l	m
r	o	p	g	s	t	o	p	h	j
m	i	l	k	e	w	i	l	d	k

My score ☐ out of 10

2 • Cover the top of the page.
   • Write as many of the words without copying
     as you can.
   • Check your spellings.

My score ☐ out of 10

24

mouth	nose	ear	hair	head
teeth	eye	lip	neck	face

1 Draw a picture of your face.
Use the words to label your picture.

2 Write the plurals of the words.

one	two
eye	eyes
lip	
face	
ear	
head	
neck	
nose	
mouth	
hair	

3 • **Draw** a monster with two heads, three eyes,
four ears, two noses and three mouths.
• **Write** a description of your monster.

Challenge Write a list of other words which
name different parts of the body.

shoe   chicken   much   chips   shop
chop   lunch   wash   wish   show

1 Write the words in the correct boxes.

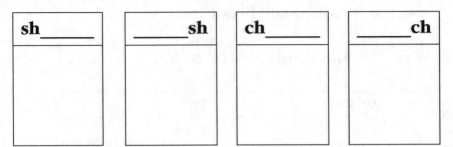

sh_____	_____sh	ch_____	_____ch

2 Which **ch** words can you eat?

_____

Which **sh** word can you wear?

_____

This **sh** word gets you wet!

_____

3 Write some more **sh** and **ch** words.

26

Target words

dine	tube	cube	mope	hate
tape	rate	wine	hope	cape

1 Write the new words.

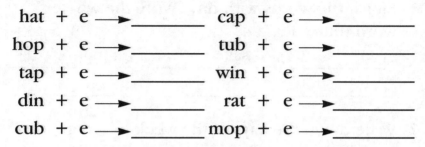

hat + e ⟶ _____   cap + e ⟶ _____

hop + e ⟶ _____   tub + e ⟶ _____

tap + e ⟶ _____   win + e ⟶ _____

din + e ⟶ _____   rat + e ⟶ _____

cub + e ⟶ _____   mop + e ⟶ _____

2 Write the new words in alphabetical order.

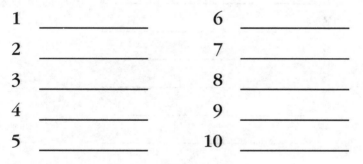

1 _____   6 _____

2 _____   7 _____

3 _____   8 _____

4 _____   9 _____

5 _____   10 _____

3 Underline the **ape** in these words.

escape   shape   tape   grape

4 Underline the **ate** in these words.

stated   crates   grater   estate   latest

27

Monday	Tuesday	Wednesday	Thursday
Friday	Saturday	Sunday	today
	yesterday	holiday	

1 Finish the words with **day**. Write the whole word underneath.

   to_____   yester_____   holi _____

   _____   _____   _____

2 Write down the days of the week in order.

   1 _____

   2 _____

   3 _____

   4 _____

   5 _____

   6 _____

   7 _____

3 Write the days of the week which begin with:

   M _____

   W _____   F _____

   S _____

   T _____

Challenge   Can you find out how the days of the week got their names?

TEST YOURSELF

mouth	escape	chips	yesterday	hope
wheel	broom	warm	partner	hair

1 Write the word that contains:

air _____   art _____

ape _____   out _____

hop _____   room _____

day _____   heel _____

hip _____   arm _____

My score ☐ out of 10

2 • Cover the top of the page.
   • Write as many of the words without copying as you can.
   • Check your spellings.

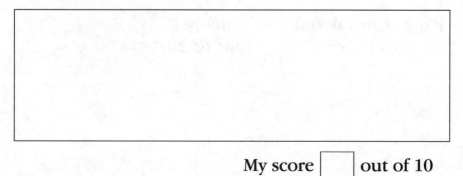

My score ☐ out of 10

31

Record sheet

Page	Completed ☑	Page	Completed ☑
3	☐	18	☐
4	☐	19	☐
5	☐	20	☐
6	☐	21	☐
7	☐	22	☐
8	☐	23	☐
9	☐	24	☐
10	☐	25	☐
11	☐	26	☐
12	☐	27	☐
13	☐	28	☐
14	☐	29	☐
15	☐	30	☐
16	☐	31	☐
17	☐		

Test Yourself

Page	Completed ☑	Score (out of 20)
9	☐	☐
17	☐	☐
24	☐	☐
31	☐	☐